S0-AFV-378

Tradition of Excellence™ Comprehensive Band Method

by Bruce Pearson & Ryan Nowlin

Dear Student:

Welcome to your study of the clarinet—an exciting adventure filled with rewards and challenges. Through careful study and regular practice, you will quickly discover the joy and satisfaction of playing beautiful music for yourself, your family, your friends, or a concert audience.

We wish you many rewarding years of clarinet playing.

Bruce Pearson
Bruce Pearson

Ryan Nowlin
Ryan Nowlin

 *Interactive Practice—the key to EXCELLENCE!*

INTERACTIVE Practice Studio　Make your practice sessions as fulfilling and productive as possible by frequently visiting your *Interactive Practice Studio* at www.kjos.com/ips.

 Hear each piece and play along! You can even change the speed. All recorded accompaniments can also be played from the DVD.

 Use the Music Writer Touch software to complete written exercises and compose your own music.

 Create recordings of your playing that you can save and email to friends, family, and your teacher.

 Download audio and video files to your computer and use them on your portable media device.

 Learn to play your first notes, care for your clarinet, and overcome challenges as you progress. Clarinet video lessons feature April Leslie and can also be viewed from the DVD.

 Access your saved recordings for playback and sharing.

 Keep an eye out for fun Extras: stories behind the songs, classical and world music recordings, practice tips, a practice journal, and more!

 Use the Tuner/Metronome during every practice session to improve your pitch and rhythm.

 Tradition of Excellence is available in SmartMusic. To subscribe go to www.smartmusic.com.

ISBN 10: 0-8497-7053-X • ISBN 13: 978-0-8497-7053-1

©2010 Kjos Music Press, Neil A. Kjos Music Company, Distributor, 4382 Jutland Drive, San Diego, California, 92117.
International copyright secured. All rights reserved. Printed in U.S.A.

Tradition of Excellence and **INTERACTIVE Practice Studio** are trademarks of Kjos Music Press.

For more detailed instruction, be sure to view the Video Lessons in your *Tradition of Excellence Interactive Practice Studio* or on the DVD. More lessons are available every time you see this icon.

Assembly

1) Put the thin end of the reed in your mouth to moisten it. Grease the corks if necessary.

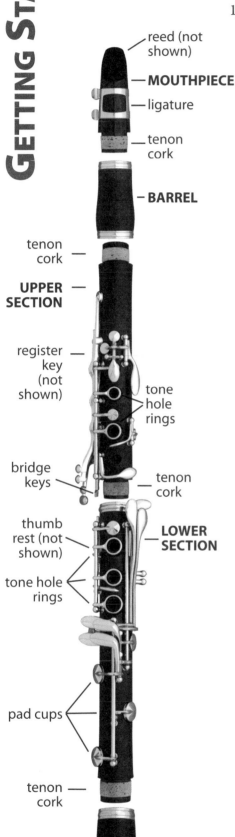

reed (not shown)

MOUTHPIECE

ligature

tenon cork

BARREL

tenon cork

UPPER SECTION

register key (not shown)

tone hole rings

bridge keys

tenon cork

thumb rest (not shown)

LOWER SECTION

tone hole rings

pad cups

tenon cork

BELL

2) Push and twist the bell onto the lower section.

3) Press down the tone hole rings to lift the bridge key on the upper section. Hold the lower section with your palm on the pad cups. Gently twist together the sections, aligning the bridge keys.

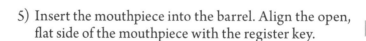

4) Twist the barrel onto the upper joint. Make sure the bridge keys stay aligned.

5) Insert the mouthpiece into the barrel. Align the open, flat side of the mouthpiece with the register key.

6) Put the ligature onto the mouthpiece. Loosen the ligature screws, slide it up slightly, and slip the reed behind it. Slide the ligature down.

7) Center the reed on the mouthpiece with a hairline of mouthpiece visible above the reed. Tighten the screws on the ligature only until snug.

Posture & Hand Position

1) Sit up straight at the edge of your chair with your feet flat on the floor.
2) Relax your body. Keep your chin parallel to the floor and your elbows away from your body.

3) Place your right thumb under the thumb rest. Keep your thumb straight. Place your left thumb over the thumbhole at a 45-degree angle.

4) Hold the clarinet directly in front of you with the bell near your knees.
5) Curve your fingers on both hands to form a relaxed "C," as if holding a tennis ball. Keep your wrists straight.

Forming an Embouchure & Making a Tone

1) Remove the mouthpiece and barrel from the clarinet.
2) Slip a piece of paper between the reed and the mouthpiece, sliding it down toward the barrel until it stops.

3) Put the tip of your thumb just under the imaginary line created by the paper. This line shows where your lower lip should be placed.
4) While holding your thumb in place on the reed, remove the paper. Form a good embouchure by shaping your mouth as if saying "whee" while you say "too."
5) Cover your bottom teeth with a small amount of your lower lip.
6) Place the mouthpiece in your mouth so your lower lip bumps against your thumb. Rest your top teeth directly on the mouthpiece. Close your lips like a drawstring. Your chin should be flat and pointed. Use a mirror to check your embouchure.
7) Take a full breath of air through your mouth and play a long, steady F♯.
8) Complete the **Mouthpiece Workout** by watching the video lesson and playing along with the recorded accompaniment (see page 1 for details).

Daily Care & Maintenance

1) Remove the ligature and reed. Place the reed in a reed holder to dry. Never store it on the mouthpiece.
2) Remove each section and carefully swab out each one. Wipe off the tenon corks and joints.
3) Wipe the outside of the clarinet with a soft, clean cloth.
4) Each time you finish caring for a part of the clarinet, return it to its proper place in the case. Latch the case.

CLARINET LESSON

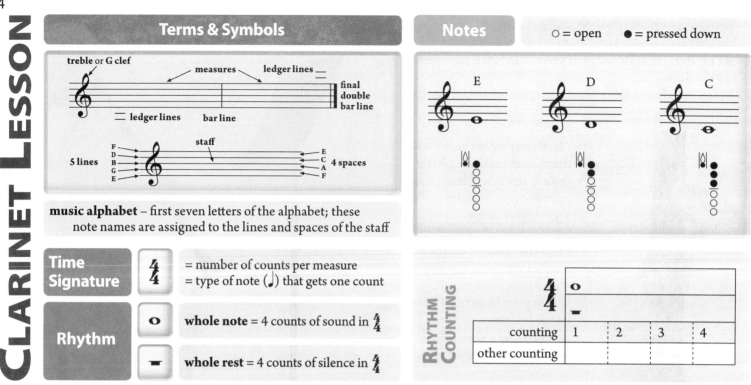

Terms & Symbols

treble or G clef
measures
ledger lines
final double bar line
ledger lines
bar line
staff
5 lines
F D B G E
E C A F
4 spaces

music alphabet – first seven letters of the alphabet; these note names are assigned to the lines and spaces of the staff

Notes

○ = open   ● = pressed down

E   D   C

Time Signature

$\frac{4}{4}$ = number of counts per measure
= type of note (♩) that gets one count

Rhythm

○ **whole note** = 4 counts of sound in $\frac{4}{4}$

▬ **whole rest** = 4 counts of silence in $\frac{4}{4}$

RHYTHM COUNTING

$\frac{4}{4}$				
counting	1	2	3	4
other counting				

To enhance practicing, use the recorded accompaniments, video lessons, and more provided in your *Tradition of Excellence Interactive Practice Studio*. See page 1 for more information.

staff & bar lines

$\frac{4}{4}$ ○ ▬

1. The "E" Express   ▶ How is your posture?

2. "D"-termination   ▶ Are you using plenty of air?

3. Music in Motion   ▶ Are you playing with a good embouchure?

4. "C" Spot Run   ▶ How is your hand position?

5. Mr. Whole Note Takes a Walk   ▶ Write the note names beneath the music before you play.

WOODWIND LESSON

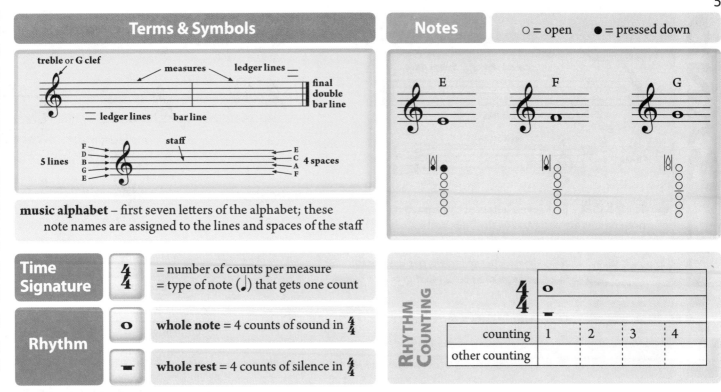

Terms & Symbols

treble or G clef — measures — ledger lines — final double bar line — ledger lines — bar line — staff — 5 lines — 4 spaces

music alphabet – first seven letters of the alphabet; these note names are assigned to the lines and spaces of the staff

Notes ○ = open ● = pressed down

E F G

Time Signature
$\frac{4}{4}$ = number of counts per measure = type of note (♩) that gets one count

Rhythm
○ **whole note** = 4 counts of sound in $\frac{4}{4}$
▬ **whole rest** = 4 counts of silence in $\frac{4}{4}$

RHYTHM COUNTING

	counting	1	2	3	4
	other counting				

To enhance practicing, use the recorded accompaniments, video lessons, and more provided in your *Tradition of Excellence Interactive Practice Studio*. See page 1 for more information.

staff & bar lines
$\frac{4}{4}$ ○ ▬

1. Woodwinds Unite ▸ How is your posture?

2. Stepping Up ▸ Are you using plenty of air?

3. Up 'n' Down 'n' Up ▸ Are you playing with a good embouchure?

4. Up We Go ▸ How is your hand position?

5. All Together, Now! ▸ Write the note names beneath the music before you play.

FULL BAND

Terms & Symbols

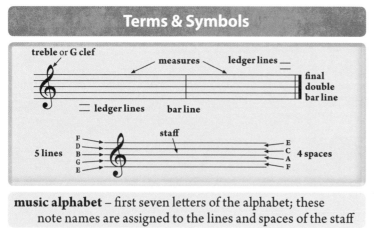

music alphabet – first seven letters of the alphabet; these note names are assigned to the lines and spaces of the staff

Notes

○ = open   ● = pressed down

Time Signature	**4/4**	= number of counts per measure = type of note (♩) that gets one count

Rhythm	○	**whole note** = 4 counts of sound in 4/4
	▬	**whole rest** = 4 counts of silence in 4/4

COUNTING & CONDUCTING

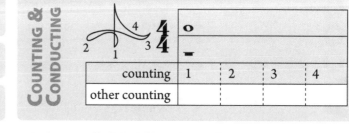

		counting	1	2	3	4
		other counting				

To enhance practicing, use the recorded accompaniments, video lessons, and more provided in your *Tradition of Excellence Interactive Practice Studio*. See page 1 for more information.

staff & bar lines

1. Away We Go!
▶ How is your posture?

2. Going Up?
▶ Are you playing with a steady air stream to produce a smooth, even sound?

3. Count Me In
▶ 1) Write the counting under the music. 2) Clap the rhythm.
3) Sing the notes using "too," the note names, or solfège. 4) Play!

4. Higher Ground
▶ Are you playing with a good embouchure?

5. Moving Around   ✓ TEST
▶ Write the note names beneath the music before you play.

6. Clarinet Private Lesson

▶ Here is how to draw a treble clef. ▶ Draw eight treble clefs on your own. Be sure they circle the second (G) line.

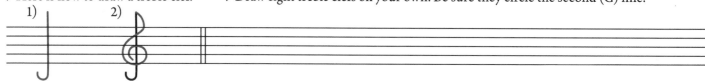

Terms & Symbols

,   **breath mark** – take a breath

sight-reading – playing or singing a piece of music for the first time

Theory & Composition

duet – piece of music featuring two different parts played or sung together

harmony – two or more notes played or sung at the same time

Rhythm

half note = 2 counts of sound in 4/4

half rest = 2 counts of silence in 4/4

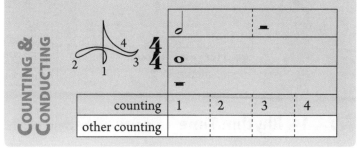

counting	1	2	3	4
other counting				

,

7. Deep Breaths

8. Rhythm Time
▶ 1) Write the counting and clap the rhythm before you play. 2) Play on the note E (Concert D).

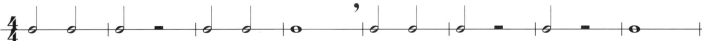

RHYTHM STUDIES: p. 44, #1-4

9. Half Note Rock

sight-reading

10. *Sight-Reading Challenge:* Steppin'
▶ Always carefully inspect music before you sight-read it.

duet, harmony

11. El Camino Mariachi — *Duet*
▶ Count, clap, sing, and play! The B part is shaded for easier reading.

12. Cuckoo ✓ TEST
Traditional

13. Excellence in Ear Training
▶ Practice with the recorded accompaniment. Listen in measures 1, 3, 5, and 7. In measures 2, 4, 6, and 8, echo what you heard. Your starting notes are shown.

W61CL

Rhythm

quarter note = 1 count of sound in 4/4

quarter rest = 1 count of silence in 4/4

COUNTING & CONDUCTING

	counting	1	2	3	4
	other counting				

Notes

D   C

14. Rhythm Time ▶ 1) Write the counting and clap the rhythm before you play. 2) Play on the note E (Concert D).

RHYTHM STUDIES: p. 44, #5-17

15. Rising Rhythms ▶ Start each note by whispering the word "too."

16. Stepping Stones ▶ Keep the air moving.

17. Rain, Rain   Traditional

18. In a Minor Mood ▶ Count, clap, sing, and play!

19. Hot Cross Buns   English Folk Song

20. Go Tell Aunt Rhodie ✓ TEST   American Folk Song

21. Clarinet Private Lesson ▶ 1) Draw a treble clef at the beginning of the staff.
2) Trace the notes and rests, and draw three more of each.

Terms & Symbols

Solo – only one person plays or sings
Soli – a small group or section plays or sings
Tutti – everyone plays or sings

repeat sign – play or sing the music again

Time Signature

C common time = 4/4

Theory & Composition

phrase – musical sentence, often 4 or 8 measures long
round – song in which the same part is played or sung by two or more groups starting at different times
composition – creation of music that can be performed later, usually from written notation

Solo, Tutti
phrase

22. Little Robin Redbreast
Traditional
1st Phrase — Solo — Tutti — 2nd Phrase — Solo — Tutti

C
:||

23. Skill Builder: Merrily We Roll Along
▶ Count, clap, sing, and play! When you reach the end of the song, repeat once from the beginning.
Traditional

round

24. Itsy Bitsy Spider — *Round*
▶ Add brackets to show the phrases.
Traditional

Soli

25. A La Rueda
Spanish Folk Song
Soli (woodwinds) — Tutti — Soli (brass/percussion) — Tutti

26. Love Somebody — *Duet*
Traditional
A.
B.

27. Good King Wenceslas ✓ TEST
Traditional English Carol
Solo/Soli — Tutti — Solo/Soli — Tutti

28. Excellence in Composition
▶ 1) Draw a treble clef. 2) Complete and play your composition.

Title _____   Composer _____

Terms & Symbols

articulation – type of attack used to play a note or group of notes

slur – articulation that connects notes of *different* pitches; indicates a very smooth sound with only the first note tongued

Notes

A

one-measure repeat sign – play or sing the previous measure again

slur

29. Warm-up: Serenity — *Round*
▶ Keep the air moving.

30. Chop Builder
▶ Roll your left hand first finger up to the A key.

31. Camptown Races
▶ Draw the missing notes in the ovals before you play.

Stephen Foster, America's first great popular songwriter, was born on the 50th anniversary of American Independence: the Fourth of July, 1826.

Stephen Foster (1826–1864) American Composer

Solo/Soli   Tutti   Solo/Soli   Tutti

32. Skill Builder
▶ Add brackets to show the phrases.

33. London Bridge — *Duet*
English Folk Song

A.

B.

34. The Frog's Song — *Round* ✓ TEST
▶ Are you rolling your left hand first finger from E to A?
Japanese Folk Song

35. Clarinet Private Lesson
▶ Are you rolling your left hand first finger up to the A key?
▶ Are you storing your reeds and swabbing your clarinet properly after each use?

MASTERING EXCELLENCE: p. 38, #1

Time Signature

$\frac{2}{4}$ = two counts per measure
= quarter note gets one count

COUNTING & CONDUCTING

counting	1	2
other counting		

Rhythm

Notes

Key Signature

sharp (♯) or flat (♭) signs placed after a clef

In these key signatures, play or sing:

no sharps or flats

every F as F sharp

every B as B flat

every B as B flat, every E as E flat

tie – marking that connects notes of the *same* pitch to make one longer note

---

tie, $\frac{2}{4}$

36. Rhythm Time
▶ 1) Write the counting and clap the rhythm before you play. 2) Play on the note D (Concert C).

RHYTHM STUDIES: p. 44, #18-20; p. 46, #41-43

---

key signature

37. Two Step
▶ The C major (Concert B♭ major) key signature, highlighted in purple, indicates no sharps or flats.

---

38. *Sight-Reading Challenge:* **Shoo Fly**
American Folk Song

---

39. Russian Folk Song — *Duet*

Beethoven bridged music history's Classical and Romantic Periods.

Ludwig van Beethoven (1770–1827)
German Composer

A.

B.

---

40. San Sereni ✓ TEST ▶ Add brackets to show the phrases.
Puerto Rican Folk Song

---

41. Excellence in Theory
▶ Add the notes and rests together to find the number of counts. A quarter note gets one count.

a) ♩ + ♩ = ___

b) ♩ + 𝅗𝅥 = ___

c) 𝄽 + ♩ + ▬ = ___

d) 𝅝 + ▬ = ___

ENSEMBLES

Theory & Composition	Terms & Symbols

trio – piece of music featuring three different parts played or sung together

introduction – opening passage of a piece of music

theme – a melody within a piece of music

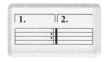

rehearsal numbers – find important places in the music using these markers

1st and 2nd endings – play or sing the 1st ending the first time through, repeat, skip the 1st ending, and play or sing the 2nd ending the second time through

fermata – hold a note or rest longer than its usual value

Concert Etiquette
—Enter the stage or performance area confidently. Make eye contact with the audience and smile.
—Stand or sit tall. Be positive and energetic. It's fun to share your music with others!

trio, introduction, theme

rehearsal numbers, 1st & 2nd endings

Solo: A   **Duet:** A + B   **Trio** or **Full Band:** A + B + C

Jingle Bells

J.S. Pierpont (1822–1893)
American Composer

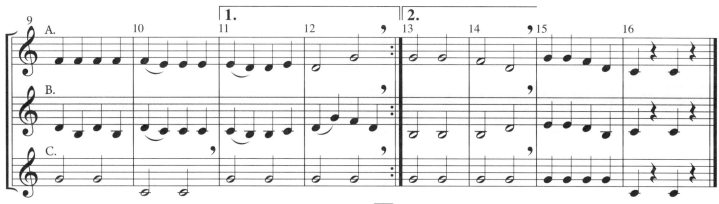

▶ Repeat back to 5 .

Jolly Old St. Nicholas

Traditional

W61CL

The Dreidel Song

Jewish Folk Song

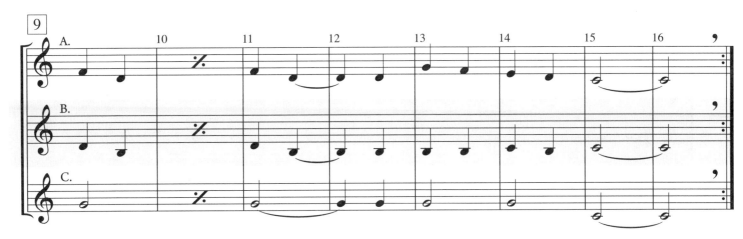

Kwanzaa Celebration

David Bobrowitz (b. 1945)
American Composer

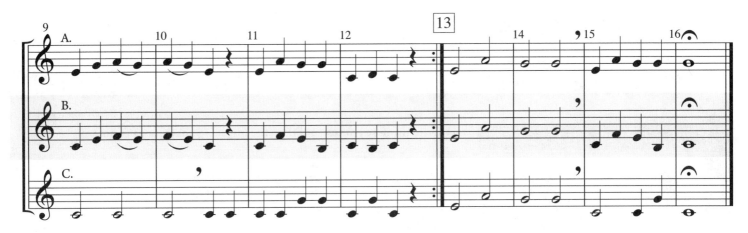

Rhythm

eighth note = ½ count of sound
in $\frac{2}{4}$, $\frac{4}{4}$, or $\mathbf{C}$

a single eighth note has a **flag**

a group of eighth notes is connected by a **beam**

COUNTING & CONDUCTING

counting	1	&	2	&	3	&	4	&
other counting								

42. Warm-up: Breath Support Challenge
▶ Take a deep breath and play with your best tone while holding the pitch for as long as you can. On which beat did you finish?

43. Epic Eighth Notes
▶ The bottom line provides the basic pulse.

Clap

44. Michael Finnegan
▶ Count, clap, sing, and play!

Irish Folk Song

1.   2.

45. Eighth Note Escapade

Clap

46. Skill Builder: Processional Dance
▶ Count, clap, sing, and play!

Renaissance Dance Music

1.   2.

47. Baja Breeze ✓ TEST

1.   2.

48. Clarinet Private Lesson
▶ 1) Write the note names. 2) Fill in the fingering chart for each note.

E

Theory & Composition **improvisation** – spontaneous composition of music through playing or singing

49. Unforgettable Eighth Notes

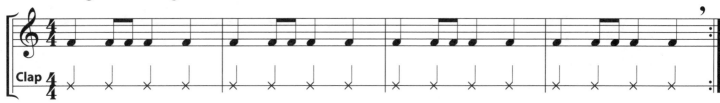

50. Mahnomen Harvest ▶ Count, clap, sing, and play!

51. Eighth Notes on the Edge

52. Now Let Me Fly ▶ Count, clap, sing, and play!

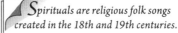

Spirituals are religious folk songs created in the 18th and 19th centuries.   American Spiritual

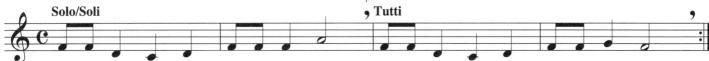

53. *Sight-Reading Challenge:* Promenade ▶ 1) Write the counting and draw the bar lines. 2) Sight-read!

54. Rio Con Brio ✔ TEST

55. Excellence in Improvisation ▶ Play along with the recorded accompaniment. Measures 1-2: Play the written notes. Measures 3-5: Improvise using the same notes.

W61CL

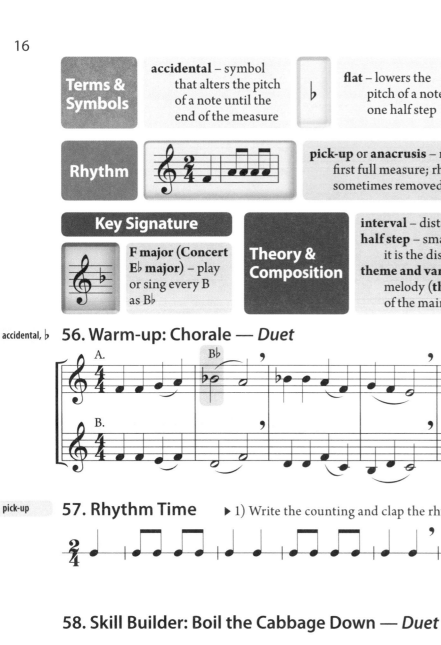

Terms & Symbols

accidental – symbol that alters the pitch of a note until the end of the measure

♭ **flat** – lowers the pitch of a note one half step

B → B♭

Rhythm

pick-up or **anacrusis** – music that comes before the first full measure; rhythmic value of the pick-up is sometimes removed from the last measure

Notes

B flat (B♭)

Key Signature

F major (Concert E♭ major) – play or sing every B as B♭

Theory & Composition

interval – distance between two pitches

half step – smallest interval used in Western music; on a piano keyboard, it is the distance from one key to the very next key—white or black

theme and variation – type of composition that begins with a main melody (**theme**) and continues with different versions (**variations**) of the main melody

---

accidental, ♭

56. Warm-up: Chorale — *Duet*

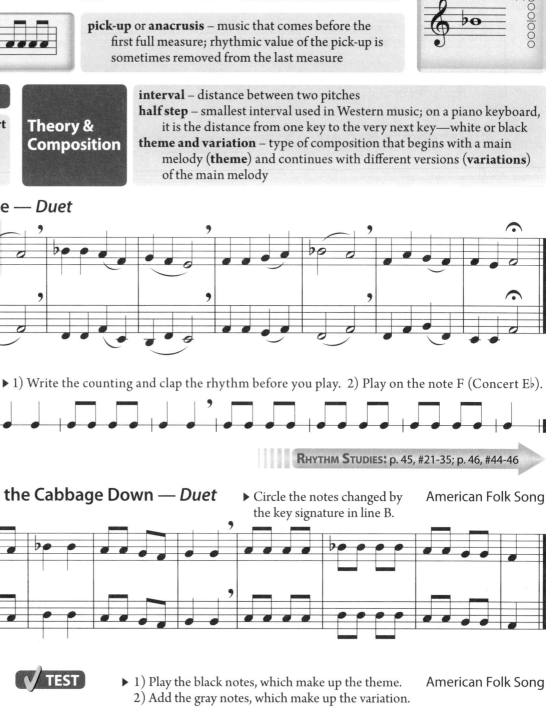

---

pick-up

57. Rhythm Time

▶ 1) Write the counting and clap the rhythm before you play. 2) Play on the note F (Concert E♭).

RHYTHM STUDIES: p. 45, #21-35; p. 46, #44-46

---

58. Skill Builder: Boil the Cabbage Down — *Duet*

▶ Circle the notes changed by the key signature in line B.

American Folk Song

---

theme & variation

59. Bingo Variations   ✓ TEST

▶ 1) Play the black notes, which make up the theme.
2) Add the gray notes, which make up the variation.

American Folk Song

---

60. Clarinet Private Lesson

▶ Are you rolling your left hand first finger up to the A key to play B♭?

MASTERING EXCELLENCE: p. 38, #2

Rhythm · **dot** – adds half the value of the note

♩. = ♩ ♪ = ♩.
2 + 1 = 2 + 1 = 3

dotted half note = 3 counts of sound in 3/4, 4/4, or C

Time Signature 3/4 = three counts per measure = quarter note gets one count

COUNTING & CONDUCTING

Terms & Symbols

dynamics – softness or loudness of a piece of music

p **piano** – soft

f **forte** – loud

	counting	1 &	2 &	3 &
	other counting			

61. Rhythm Time
▶ 1) Write the counting and clap the rhythm before you play. 2) Play on the note F (Concert E♭).

RHYTHM STUDIES: p. 46, #49-53

62. Encounter in Three
▶ Circle the notes changed by the key signature.

63. Skill Builder: A Simple Waltz

64. *Sight-Reading Challenge:* Theme from "Cambridge Overture"

Anne McGinty is one of the most prolific female composers of band music and has over 225 pieces published for band, orchestra, and flute.

Anne McGinty (b. 1945)
American Composer

From *Cambridge Overture* (Q881077), ©1991 Edmondson & McGinty. All rights assigned Queenwood/Kjos 2002. Used with permission.

65. I've Just Come From Sydney ✔ TEST

Australian Folk Song

66. Excellence in Composition: Carnival of Venice

Italian Folk Song

▶ 1) Play the theme. 2) Add eighth notes after some of the quarter notes to compose a variation as in **59. Bingo Variations**. **Bonus:** Improvise a variation!

| Terms & Symbols | tempo – speed of a piece of music
Andante – walking tempo; slower than **Moderato**
Moderato – medium tempo
Allegro – fast tempo | *mp*
mf | *mezzo piano* –
medium soft
mezzo forte –
medium loud | accent –
emphasize
the note |

67. Warm-up: Lullaby

Andante

Welsh Folk Song

68. Ezekiel Saw the Wheel — *Duet*

Allegro

American Spiritual

69. Rhythm Time ▶1) Write the counting and clap the rhythm before you play. 2) Play on the note C (Concert B♭).

Moderato

RHYTHM STUDIES: p. 46, #54-58

70. *Sight-Reading Challenge:* Streets of Laredo

Laredo is a city in Texas on the Mexican border.

American Folk Song

Moderato

71. Skill Builder: Donkey Riding ▶ 1) Add brackets to show the phrases.
2) Add a breath mark between the phrases.

Canadian Folk Song

Moderato

72. Theme from "The Nutcracker" ✓ TEST

Tchaikovsky first studied to be a lawyer but eventually became a full-time composer thanks to the support of a wealthy patron.

Peter Ilyich Tchaikovsky
(1840–1893)
Russian Composer

Andante

73. Clarinet Private Lesson

SOLO

Concert Etiquette — As a soloist, at the end of your performance, bow to acknowledge the applause of the audience, then gratefully gesture towards your accompanist so that he or she may also receive recognition from the audience.

In addition to his work as a composer and author, Ryan Nowlin is a music teacher, horn player, and singer.

The Good Life
Solo with Piano Accompaniment

Ryan Nowlin (b. 1978)
American Composer

W61CL

BAND PIECES

Theory & Composition	Terms & Symbols

chord – two or more notes sounded at the same time

closing – last measures of a composition, often containing music added to give a feeling of finality

2 — **long rest** or **multiple-measure rest** – rest for the number of measures indicated

Concert Etiquette

—If you make a mistake, never let it show. Keep playing or singing as if nothing happened.
—When you are finished, graciously accept the audience's applause. Leave the stage area confidently.

chord

Warm-up: Tone, Balance, and Tuning

▶ There are many ways to perform a warm-up; follow the instructions given by your director.

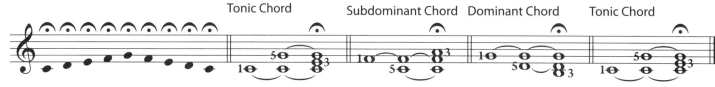

closing

March Across the Seas

Bruce Pearson (b. 1942) and
Ryan Nowlin (b. 1978)
American Composers

Bruce Pearson played clarinet and saxophone as well as baseball and hockey into his college years before becoming a music teacher, author, composer, and conductor.

Water Music was written for a royal boat party on England's Thames River. The orchestra played from one barge while King George I and friends listened from another vessel close by.

Procession
from "Water Music"

George Frideric Handel (1685–1759)
English Composer
arr. Ryan Nowlin

▶ In $\frac{2}{4}$, $\frac{3}{4}$, and other time signatures, ▬ indicates a full measure of rest.

Banana Boat Song

Jamaican Folk Song
arr. Ryan Nowlin

long rest

Indigo Rock

Bruce Pearson & Ryan Nowlin
American Composers

W61CL

Terms & Symbols

crescendo – gradually louder
decrescendo – gradually softer

♮ natural – cancels a flat (♭) or sharp (♯)

divisi (div.) – some performers play or sing the top notes while others play or sing the bottom notes

unisono (unis.) – everyone plays or sings the same notes

Notes

B flat (B♭)   B alternate   A   G

74. Warm-up: "Werde munter" — Duet
Andante

Johann Schop was a virtuoso violinist but also played cornet and trombone. This melody by Schop was used by J.S. Bach in his famous **Cantata 147**.

Johann Schop (1590–1667)
German Composer

75. Fais Dodo
Andante

French Folk Song

76. Baroque March
Moderato

Though considered an English composer, Handel was born in Germany.

George Frideric Handel (1685–1759)
English Composer

77. La Bamba
▶ Circle the notes changed by the key signature.

divisi, unisono, ♮

Allegro   div.   unis.

Mexican Folk Song

78. Skill Builder ✔ TEST
Moderato

79. Clarinet Private Lesson
▶ Use the alternate B fingering on notes with ∗ .

A

B   A G

MASTERING EXCELLENCE: p. 38, #3

Theory & Composition

whole step – interval consisting of two half steps

major scale – series of whole (w) and half (h) steps in the following pattern:

1 2 3 4 5 6 7 8
w w h w w w h

arpeggio – notes of a chord sounded one after another

orchestration – choice of instruments used to play the music

80. Going Up or Down?

Andante

81. Just By Accident

▶ Use the alternate B fingering on notes with ∗ .

Andante

82. *Sight-Reading Challenge:*
Theme from "Orpheus In the Underworld"

In addition to composing, Jacques Offenbach was a fine cellist.

Jacques Offenbach (1819–1880)
French Composer

Allegro

83. C Major Scale, Arpeggio, and Chords (Concert B♭ Major)

major scale, arpeggio

Major Scale   Arpeggio   Chords **div.**

84. Crescent Moon Rising

orchestration

Andante

Chinese Folk Song

Orchestration: Full Band ———— Woodwinds & Percussion ———— Brass & Percussion ———— Full Band ————

85. Skill Builder   ✓ TEST

▶ Also play with other articulations: A)   B)   C)

Moderato

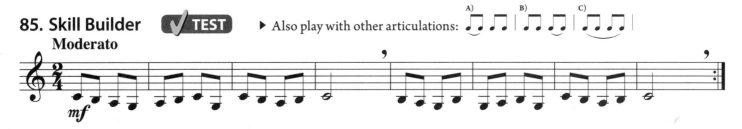

86. Excellence in Improvisation

▶ Play along with the recorded accompaniment. Measures 1-2: Play the written notes.

Measures 3-5: Improvise using [notation] .

1 (Play 4 times)   2   3 Improvise – – – – – 4 – – – – – – – – – 5 – –

Terms & Symbols

staccato – shorten the note

Notes

94. Warm-up: Tone Builder
Andante

95. F Major Scale, Arpeggio, and Chords (Concert E♭ Major)
Major Scale — Arpeggio — Chords — div.

96. When the Saints Go Marching In
Allegro

When the Saints Go Marching In is often performed in a Dixieland jazz style. Dixieland originated in New Orleans, Louisiana in the early 20th century.

American Spiritual

97. Musette
Allegro
Solo/Soli — Tutti

Bach's death marked the end of the Baroque Period.

Johann Sebastian Bach (1685–1750)
German Composer

staccato

98. Bella Bimba
Moderato

Italian Folk Song

99. Skill Builder ✓ TEST
Moderato

▶ Use the alternate F♯ and B fingerings on notes with ✱.

100. Excellence in Ear Training

▶ Practice with the recorded accompaniment. Listen in measures 1, 3, 5, and 7. In measures 2, 4, 6, and 8, echo what you heard. Your starting notes are shown.

1 Listen 2 Play 3 Listen 4 Play 5 Listen 6 Play 7 Listen 8 Play

Rhythm

dotted quarter note =
1½ counts of sound in
²⁄₄, ³⁄₄, ⁴⁄₄, or **C**

COUNTING & CONDUCTING

	counting	1	&	2	&
	other counting				

Terms & Symbols

Da Capo al Fine (D.C. al Fine) – go back to the beginning of the piece and play or sing until the *Fine*

Notes

101. Warm-up: Chop Builders
Andante

102. Low Down
▸ Make sure to use plenty of air as you play the lower notes.
Andante

103. Dotted Quarters
▸ The bottom line provides the basic pulse.
Moderato

Clap

RHYTHM STUDIES: p. 45, #36-40; p. 46, #47-48, 59-60

D.C. al Fine

104. Alouette
▸ Orchestrate by writing in the instruments that will play each four-measure section.

French Canadian Folk Song

Allegro   *Fine*

D.C. al Fine

105. Ronde   ✓ **TEST**

Tielman Susato was a Renaissance composer, trumpet player, and music publisher. He wrote mostly dance music, including Ronde.

Tielman Susato (c. 1500–c. 1562)
Flemish (Belgian) Composer
Moderato

106. Clarinet Private Lesson

MASTERING EXCELLENCE: p. 39, #5

Terms & Symbols | **Maestoso** – majestically | **Notes**

107. Soar!

Andante

108. Skill Builder ▶ The lower notes are optional.

Moderato

109. *Sight-Reading Challenge:* Theme from "The Red Balloon"

Anne McGinty (b. 1945)
American Composer

Moderato

From *The Red Balloon* (Q882119), ©1993 Edmondson & McGinty. All rights assigned Queenwood/Kjos 2002. Used with permission.

Maestoso

110. Trumpet Voluntary — *Duet* ✓ **TEST**

Trumpet Voluntary is also known as **Prince of Denmark's March** and was originally composed for harpsichord.

Jeremiah Clarke
(c. 1674–1707)
English Composer

Introduction

A. **Maestoso**

Theme

B.

A.

B.

111. Excellence in Theory ▶ Add the notes and rests together to find the number of counts. A quarter note gets one count.

a) ♩ + ♩. = ___   b) 𝅗𝅥 + 𝄽 = ___   c) ♩. + ♩ + ♫ = ___   d) 𝄽 + ♪ + ♩. = ___

112. Warm-up: Range, Tone, and Tuning

113. Skill Builder

114. Look Before You Leap

115. In the Bleak Midwinter — *Duet*

20th Century composer Gustav Holst was a professional trombonist. *In the Bleak Midwinter* was originally written for congregational singing.

Gustav Holst (1874–1934)
English Composer

116. Theme from "Symphony No. 9" ✓ TEST

Beethoven was completely deaf when he wrote Symphony No. 9 in 1824.

Ludwig van Beethoven
(1770–1827)
German Composer

117. Clarinet Private Lesson

▶ 1) Write the note names. 2) Fill in the fingering chart for each note.

118. Lone Star Waltz ▶ 1) Orchestrate by writing in the instruments that will play each two-measure section of the music. 2) Add dynamics.

Erin Watson was born in Wichita Falls, Texas, the Lone Star State. She plays violin, piano, and accordion. She studied with famed American composer Joan Tower.

Erin A. Watson (b. 1977)
American Composer

Andante

119. *Sight-Reading Challenge:* Yangtze Boatman Chantey

Andante ▶ 1) Add brackets to show the phrases. 2) Add a breath mark between the phrases. Chinese Folk Song

120. E–Z Does It

Andante

121. Mary Ann — *Duet*

Moderato

Calypso began in early 20th century Caribbean communities where slaves used music to communicate without their master's understanding. Today, the music often features guitar, steel drums, and other percussion instruments accompanying the vocals.

Calypso Song

122. Skill Builder: Happy Little Donkey — *Round* ✓ TEST

Andante

American Folk Song

123. Excellence in Ear Training ▶ Practice with the recorded accompaniment. Listen in measures 1, 3, 5, and 7. In measures 2, 4, 6, and 8, echo what you heard. Your starting notes are shown.

1 Listen   2 Play   3 Listen   4 Play   5 Listen   6 Play   7 Listen   8 Play

Clarinet Technique — **crossing the break** – moving between the lower and higher registers of the clarinet

Terms & Symbols — *ritardando* (*ritard.* or *rit.*) – gradually slow the tempo

crossing the break

124. Warm-up: Chop Builders

Moderato

125. Oh Yeah!

Andante

126. Skill Builder

 ▶ Keep your right hand fingers down throughout this exercise.

Andante

ritardando

127. Theme from "The Sleeping Beauty"

▶ Circle the notes changed by the key signature.
▶ R.H. down = keep right hand fingers down.

In 1891, Tchaikovsky traveled to America for the opening of Carnegie Hall in New York City.

Peter Ilyich Tchaikovsky
(1840–1893)
Russian Composer

Allegro

rit.

128. Amazing Grace

American Folk Song

Andante

rit.

129. Clarinet Private Lesson

▶ Keep your right hand fingers down throughout this exercise.

Mastering Excellence: p. 39, #6

| Rhythm | 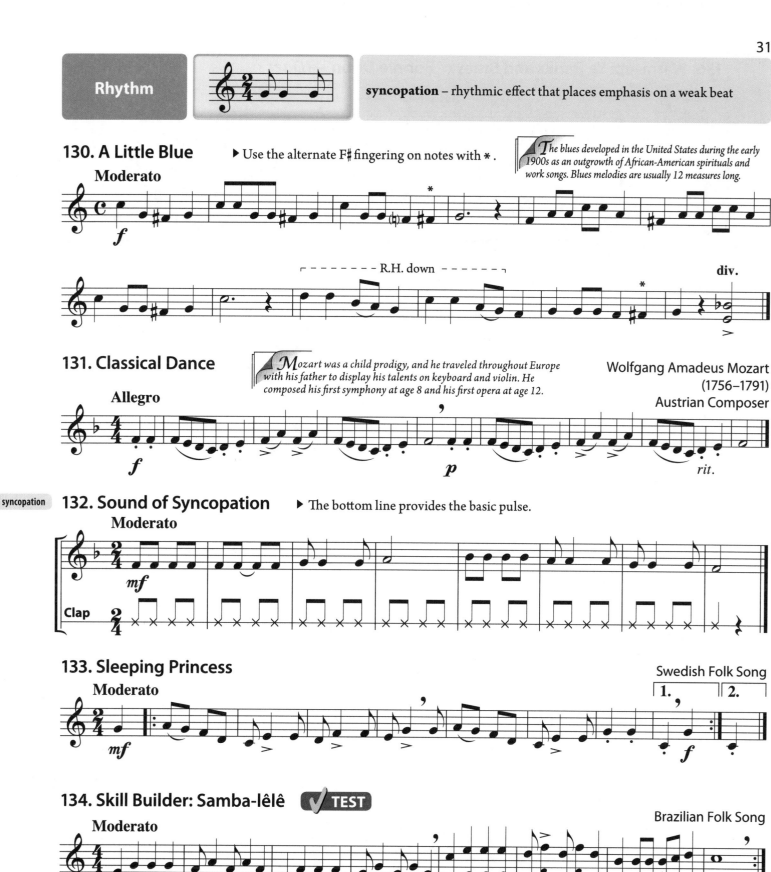 | **syncopation** – rhythmic effect that places emphasis on a weak beat |

130. A Little Blue

▸ Use the alternate F♯ fingering on notes with *.

The blues developed in the United States during the early 1900s as an outgrowth of African-American spirituals and work songs. Blues melodies are usually 12 measures long.

Moderato

- - - - - - R.H. down - - - - - -   div.

131. Classical Dance

Mozart was a child prodigy, and he traveled throughout Europe with his father to display his talents on keyboard and violin. He composed his first symphony at age 8 and his first opera at age 12.

Wolfgang Amadeus Mozart
(1756–1791)
Austrian Composer

Allegro

132. Sound of Syncopation

▸ The bottom line provides the basic pulse.

syncopation

Moderato

Clap

133. Sleeping Princess

Swedish Folk Song

Moderato

134. Skill Builder: Samba-lêlê   ✓ TEST

Brazilian Folk Song

Moderato

135. Excellence in Theory

A. Write these tempo marks in the correct blanks: slowest ⟵————————⟶ fastest

Andante Allegro Moderato   _____ _____ _____

B. Write these dynamic marks in the correct blanks: softest ⟵————————⟶ loudest

mf   *p*   *f*   *mp*   _____ _____ _____ _____

136. Warm-up: Ye Banks and Braes o' Bonnie Doon — *Duet*
Scottish Folk Song

137. Open the Door for Me!
▶ Add brackets to show the phrases.
South African Folk Song

138. Shepherd's Hey
*Australian-born composer Percy Grainger (1882-1961) is well known for his arrangements of English folk songs and country dances. His 1918 version of **Shepherd's Hey** for concert band shows Grainger's skills in orchestration, and is part of the band world's standard repertoire.*
English Folk Song

139. The Yellow Rose of Texas
American Folk Song

140. Manhattan Beach March ✓ TEST
▶ Use the alternate F♯ fingering on the note with ∗.
Sousa played piano, violin, flute, cornet, trombone, and baritone. He is most remembered for his marches, and is known as "The March King."
John Philip Sousa
(1854–1932)
American Composer

ENSEMBLE

The term "military band" was historically used to designate an instrumental ensemble made up of woodwinds, brass, and percussion, much like today's concert band. **Ecossaise for Military Band** *was originally written by Beethoven in 1810 for this type of ensemble. The work is a* **contradance**, *a lively dance-inspired composition in* **2/4**. *In a contradance, couples faced each other in two lines. It was a Classical Period predecessor to more modern forms such as square dancing.*

Solo: A   **Duet:** A + B   **Trio** or **Full Band:** A + B + C

Ecossaise for Military Band

▶ 1st x = first time through. 2nd x = second time through.

Ludwig van Beethoven (1770–1827)
German Composer
arr. Bruce Pearson

W61CL

BAND PIECES

Theory & Composition

ternary form – music with three sections: Section A, followed by a contrasting Section B, then Section A again

trio – third theme in a march, typically a contrasting section

ternary form

Concert Etiquette

Dress nicely for every performance. If no specific guidelines are given by your director, be sure to ask what is appropriate. When you look your best, the audience will more fully appreciate your playing or singing.

See, the Conquering Hero Comes
from "Judas Maccabaeus"

Judas Maccabaeus, composed in 1746, is one of Handel's most famous oratorios. This piece majestically commemorates the title character's victorious return from battle.

George Frideric Handel (1685–1759)
English Composer
arr. Ryan Nowlin

Riverside March

Ryan Nowlin (b. 1978)
American Composer

▶ Notice the key signature changes at 27 and 47.

W61CL

SOLO

German dance is a general term for triple meter dances of the late 18th and early 19th centuries. This German dance was written around 1795 or 1796 when Beethoven was becoming famous both as a composer and virtuoso pianist.

German Dance
Solo with Piano Accompaniment

Ludwig van Beethoven (1770-1827)
German Composer
arr. Bruce Pearson and Ryan Nowlin

MASTERING EXCELLENCE

1. After page 10, #35
▶ Are you rolling your left hand first finger up to the A key?

Basic Preparatory Exercise

Advanced Preparatory Exercise

Mastering Excellence

2. After page 16, #60
▶ Roll your left hand first finger up to the A key to play A and B♭.

Basic Preparatory Exercise

Advanced Preparatory Exercise

Mastering Excellence

3. After page 22, #79
▶ Use the alternate B fingering on notes with ✱.

Basic Preparatory Exercise

Advanced Preparatory Exercise

Mastering Excellence

4. After page 24, #93
▶ Use the alternate F♯ fingering on notes with ✱.

Basic Preparatory Exercise

Advanced Preparatory Exercise

Mastering Excellence

5. After Page 26, #106

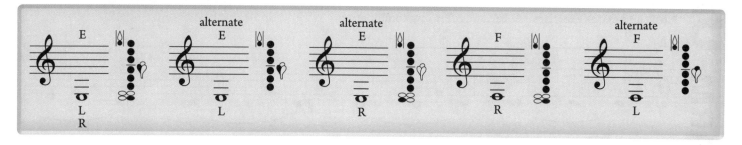

Basic Preparatory Exercise

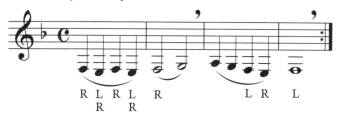

Advanced Preparatory Exercise

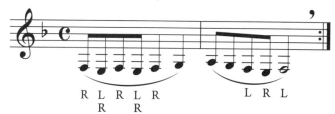

Mastering Excellence

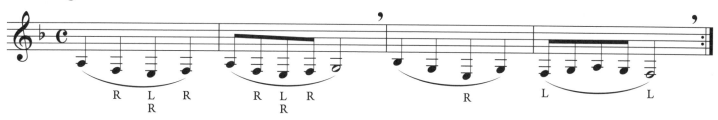

6. After page 30, #129

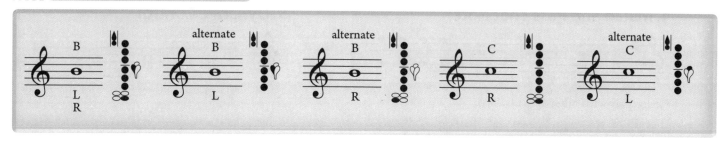

Basic Preparatory Exercise

Advanced Preparatory Exercise

Mastering Excellence

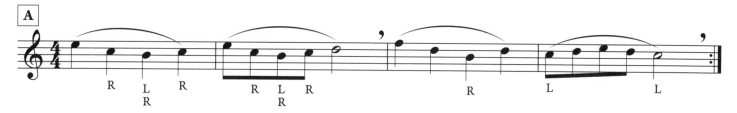

▶ Keep your right hand down throughout this exercise.

GREAT WARM-UPS

Chop Builders

▸ Mix and match exercises 1A, 2A, and 3A in any combination.

1A.

2A.

3A.

1B, 2B, 3B. ▸ Use this line to accompany 1A, 2A, and 3A.

4. Match and Pass That Note

▸ Also play with other articulations:

5. Dynamic Control

C Major Warm-Up (Concert B♭ Major)

1. C Major Scale and Arpeggios

2. C Major Technique Study

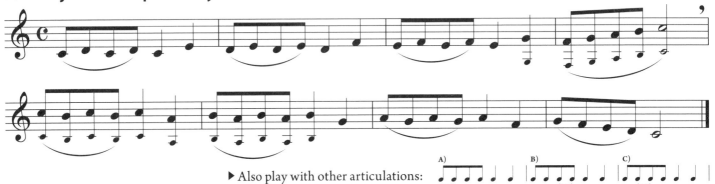

▸ Also play with other articulations:

3. C Major Balance and Tuning Study

4. C Major Chorale: All Grace and Thanksgiving

Ryan Nowlin (b. 1978)
American Composer

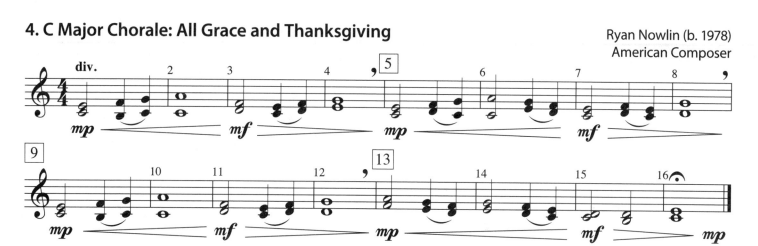

F Major Warm-Up (Concert E♭ Major)

1. F Major Scale and Arpeggios

2. F Major Technique Study

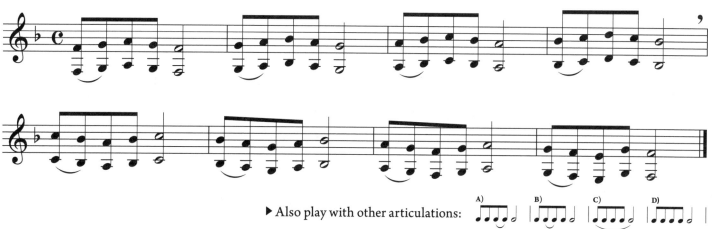

▶ Also play with other articulations:

3. F Major Balance and Tuning Study

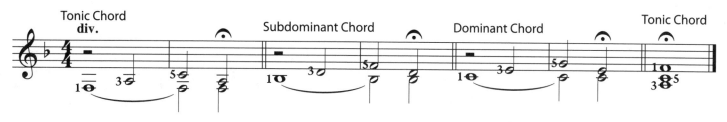

4. F Major Chorale: Make a Joyful Sound

Ryan Nowlin (b. 1978)
American Composer

G Major Warm-Up (Concert F Major)

1. G Major Scale and Arpeggios

2. G Major Technique Study

▶ Also play with other articulations:

3. G Major Balance and Tuning Study

4. G Major Chorale: Celebration and Honor

Ryan Nowlin (b. 1978)
American Composer

SCALE STUDIES

Theory & Composition **chromatic scale** – series of 12 ascending or descending half steps

▶ For notes you do not know, refer to the fingering chart.

1. C Major Scale, Arpeggios, and Thirds (Concert B♭ Major)

2. F Major Scale, Arpeggios, and Thirds (Concert E♭ Major)

3. G Major Scale, Arpeggios, and Thirds (Concert F Major)

4. B♭ Major Scale, Arpeggios, and Thirds (Concert A♭ Major)

chromatic scale

5. Chromatic Scale

W61CL

RHYTHM STUDIES

4/4 or C

RESOURCES

World Map

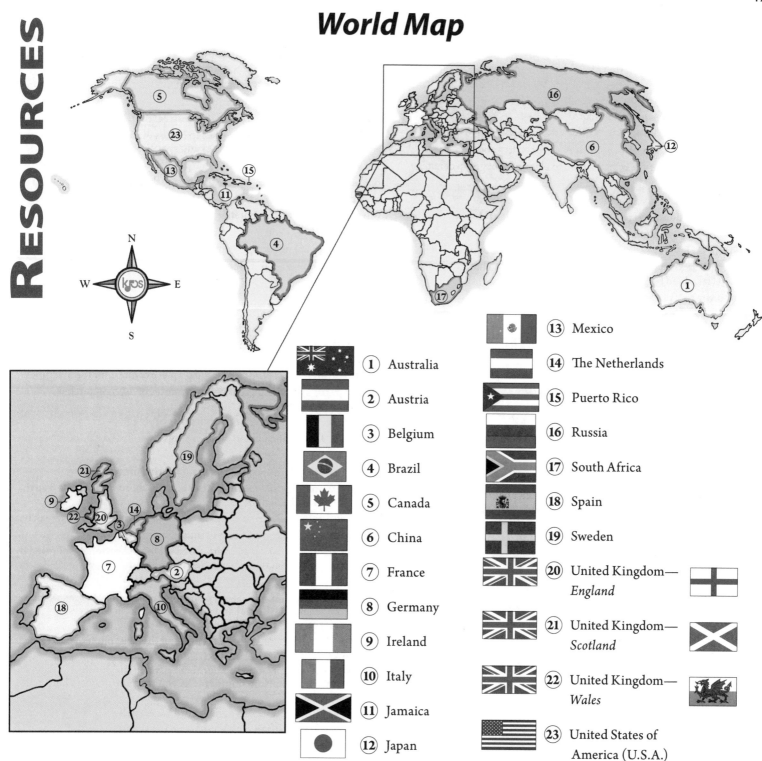

① Australia	⑬ Mexico
② Austria	⑭ The Netherlands
③ Belgium	⑮ Puerto Rico
④ Brazil	⑯ Russia
⑤ Canada	⑰ South Africa
⑥ China	⑱ Spain
⑦ France	⑲ Sweden
⑧ Germany	⑳ United Kingdom—*England*
⑨ Ireland	㉑ United Kingdom—*Scotland*
⑩ Italy	㉒ United Kingdom—*Wales*
⑪ Jamaica	㉓ United States of America (U.S.A.)
⑫ Japan	

About the Clarinet

The clarinet descended from the *chalumeau* (pronounced "sha - loo - moh"), a popular European instrument in the 1600s. The lower range of today's clarinet is called the "chalumeau register."

In the early 1700s, the Denner family of German instrument makers invented and began selling clarinets. The major improvement from the chalumeau was the register key, which facilitated higher notes. In fact, the name "clarinet" is derived from the Italian for "little trumpet."

In the 1840s, a French clarinetist named Hyacinthe Klosé adapted the Boehm system of flute fingering to the clarinet, and instrument maker Louis-Auguste Buffet constructed the new model. The fingerings have been further refined into the arrangement of holes and keys seen on most modern clarinets.

FUN FACTS

▸ Wolfgang Amadeus Mozart considered the clarinet to be closest in quality to the human voice.

▸ Clarinets range in size, from the tiny (and very rare) piccolo clarinet to the huge contrabass clarinet. They are used around the world in many styles of classical, jazz, and folk music.

▸ Check out these clarinetists: Larry Combs, Eddie Daniels, Stanley Drucker, Benny Goodman, Thea King, Mitchell Lurie, and Richard Stolzman.

Glossary/Index

Timeline

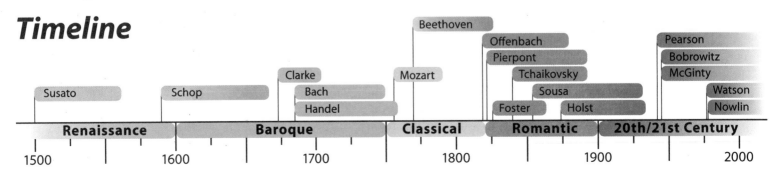